GREEN DAY / GUITAR

© 2006 BY FABER MUSIC LTD
FIRST PUBLISHED BY FABER MUSIC LTD IN 2006
3 QUEEN SQUARE, LONDON WC1N 3AU

CD RECORDED BY
TOM FLEMING (GUITARS)
NEIL WILLIAMS (BASS)
DARRIN MOONEY (DRUMS)
ELYSIAN QUARTET (STRINGS)
RECORDED AT THE MEWS RECORDING STUDIOS, LONDON
DAVE CLARKE (RECORDING & MIX ENGINEER)
www.themewsrecordingstudios.com

EDITED BY LUCY HOLLIDAY & OLLY WEEKS
ARRANGED & ENGRAVED BY TOM FLEMING

DESIGNED BY LYDIA MERRILLS-ASHCROFT & DOMINIC BROOKMAN
PICTURES FROM REDFERNS MUSIC PICTURE LIBRARY

PRINTED IN ENGLAND BY CALIGRAVING LTD

ISBN 0-571-52548-2

TO BUY FABER MUSIC PUBLICATIONS OR TO FIND OUT ABOUT THE FULL RANGE OF TITLES AVAILABLE,
PLEASE CONTACT YOUR LOCAL MUSIC RETAILER OR FABER MUSIC SALES ENQUIRIES:
FABER MUSIC LTD, BURNT MILL, ELIZABETH WAY, HARLOW, CM20 2HX ENGLAND
TEL: +44(0)1279 82 89 82 FAX: +44(0)1279 82 89 83
SALES@FABERMUSIC.COM FABERMUSIC.COM

TRACK 3
BACKING TRACK 12

AMERICAN IDIOT

WORDS AND MUSIC BY BILLIE JOE ARMSTRONG, MICHAEL PRITCHARD AND FRANK E. WRIGHT III

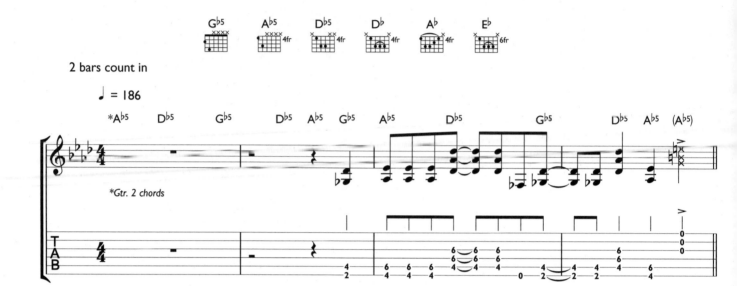

2 bars count in

♩ = 186

*Gtr. 2 chords

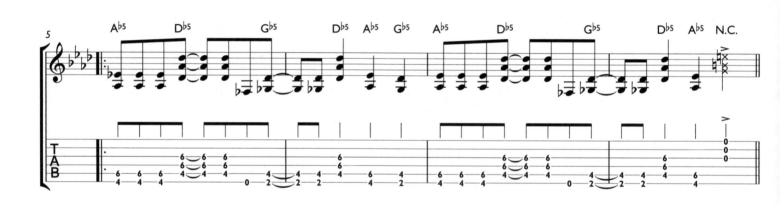

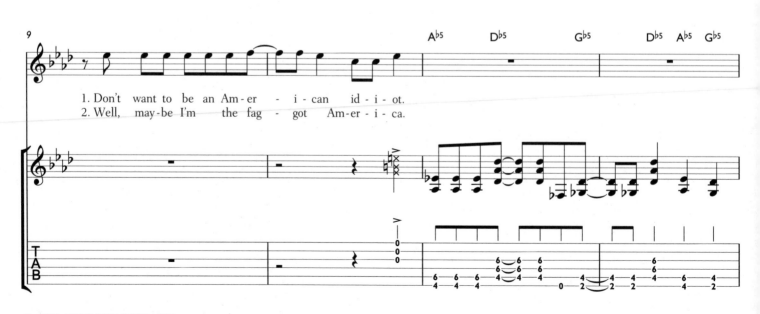

1. Don't want to be an Am-er-i-can id-i-ot.
2. Well, may-be I'm the fag-got Am-er-i-ca.

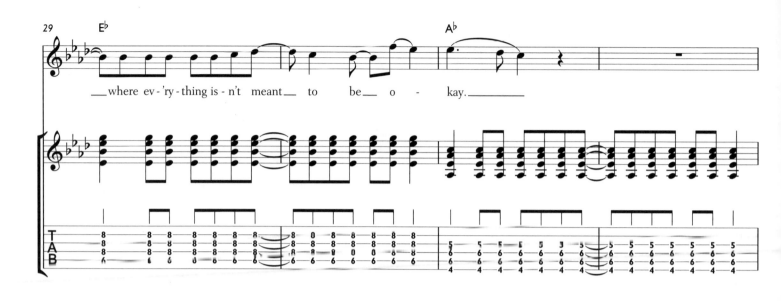

where ev - 'ry - thing is - n't meant to be o - kay.

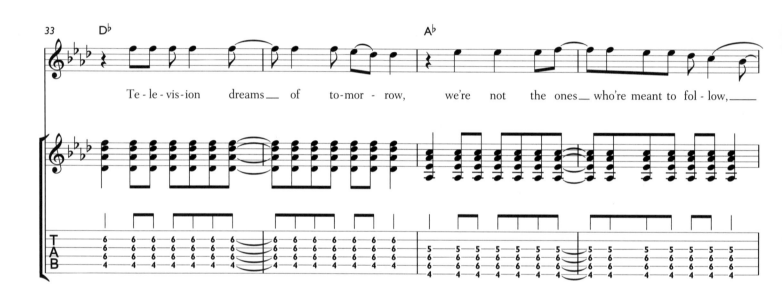

Te - le - vis - ion dreams of to-mor - row, we're not the ones who're meant to fol - low,

To Coda

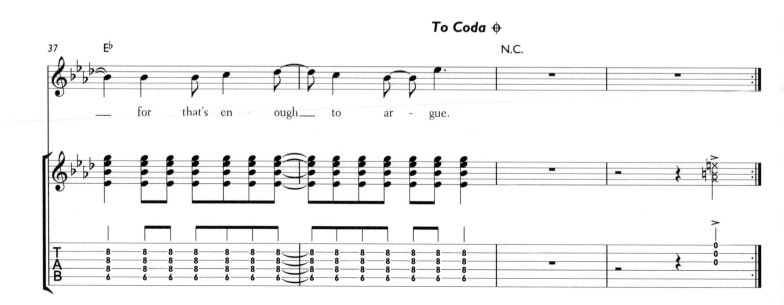

for that's en ough to ar - gue.

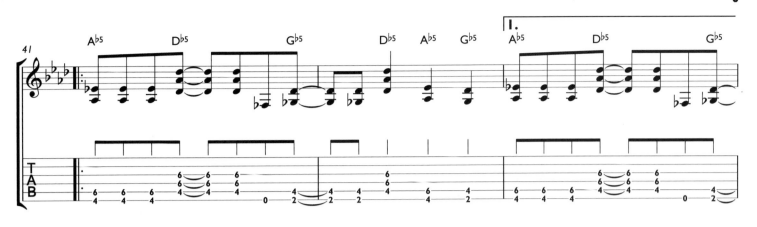

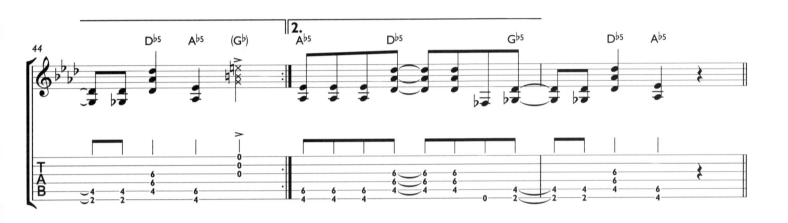

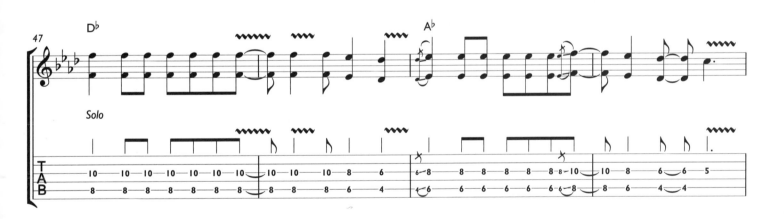

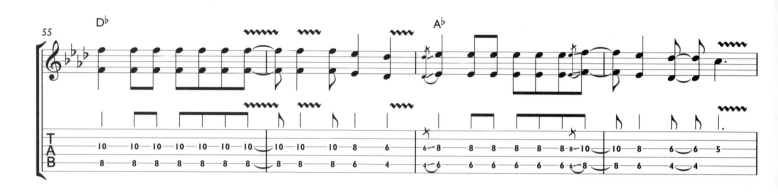

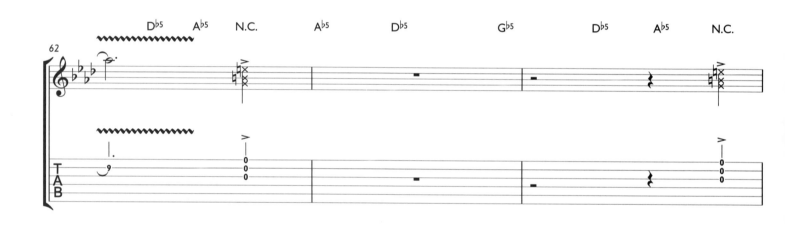

Don't want to be an Am-er - i-can id-i-ot, one na-tion con-trolled___ by the med-i-a.

Information age of hysteria — it's going out to idiot America.

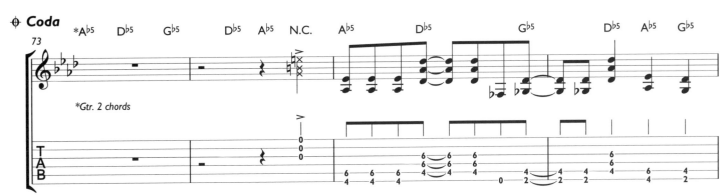

*Gtr. 2 chords

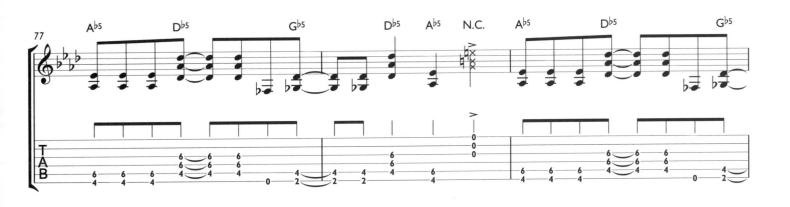

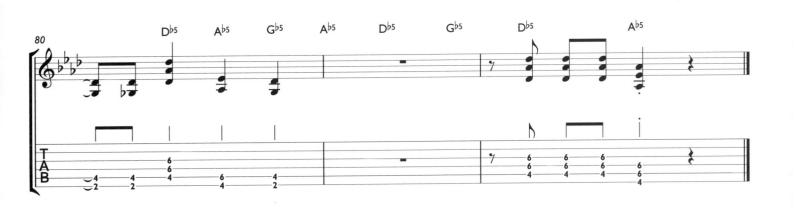

TRACK 4
BACKING TRACK 13

BASKET CASE

WORDS AND MUSIC BY BILLIE JOE ARMSTRONG, FRANK E. WRIGHT III AND MICHAEL PRITCHARD

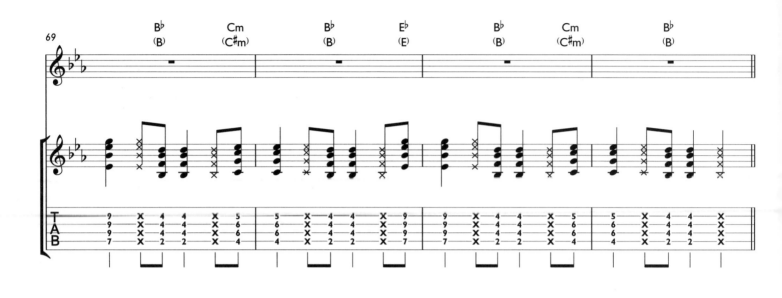

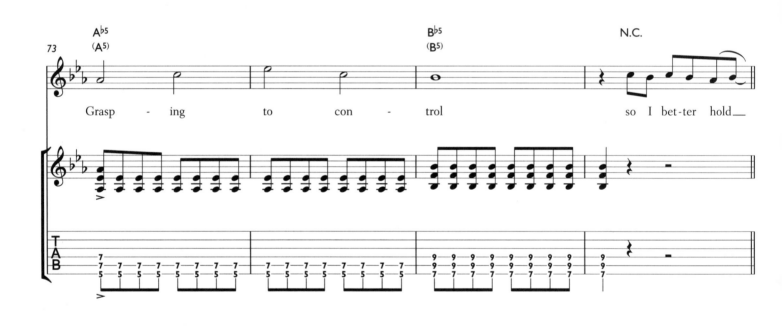

Grasp - ing to con - trol   so I bet-ter hold

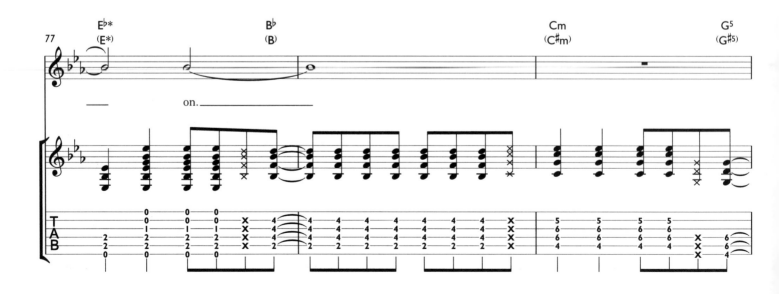

— on.

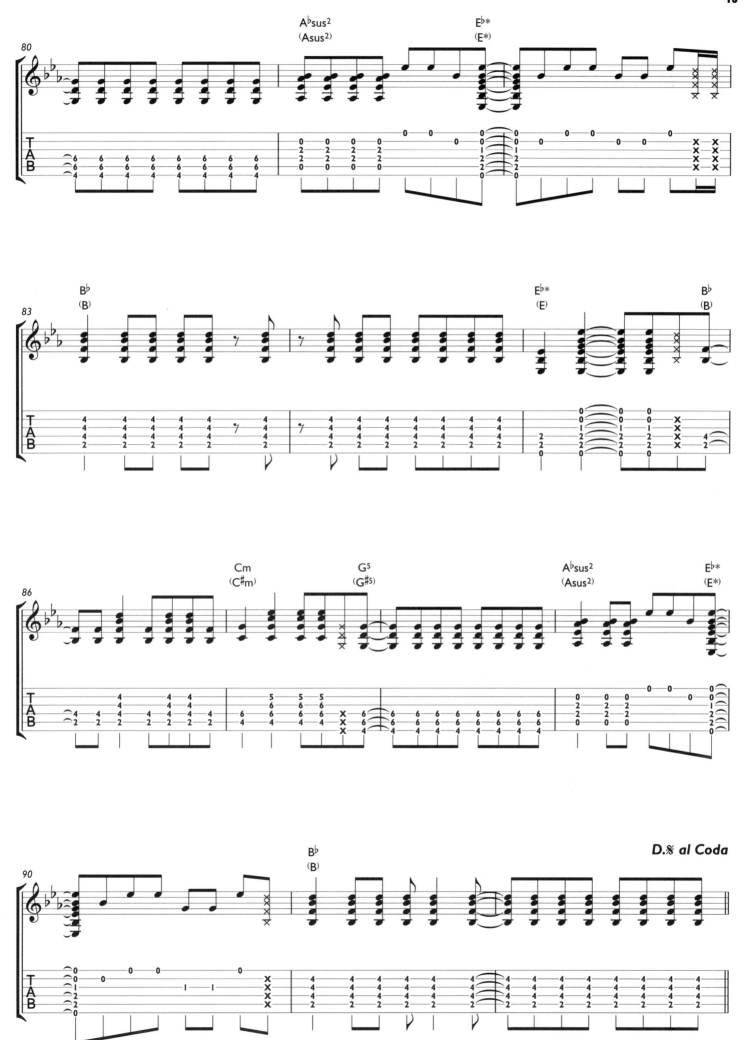

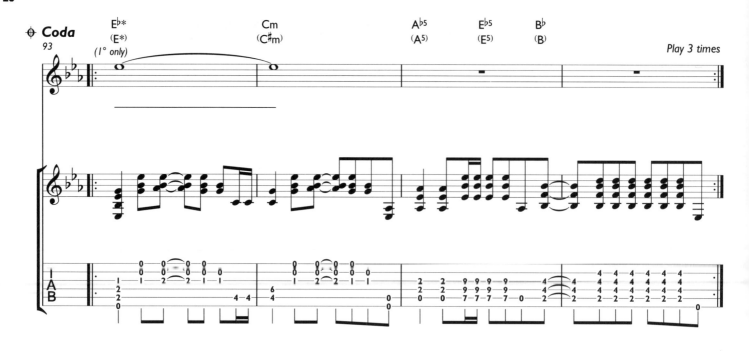

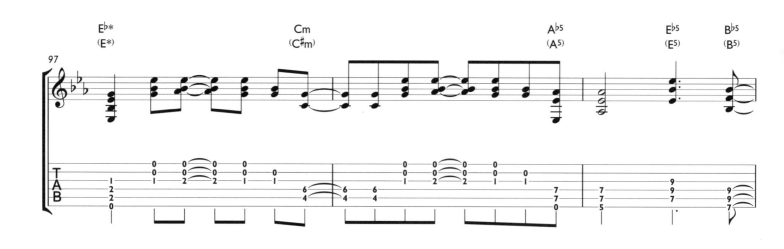

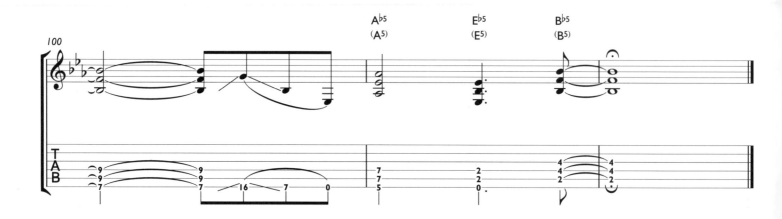

BOULEVARD OF BROKEN DREAMS

WORDS AND MUSIC BY BILLIE JOE ARMSTRONG, MICHAEL PRITCHARD AND FRANK E. WRIGHT III

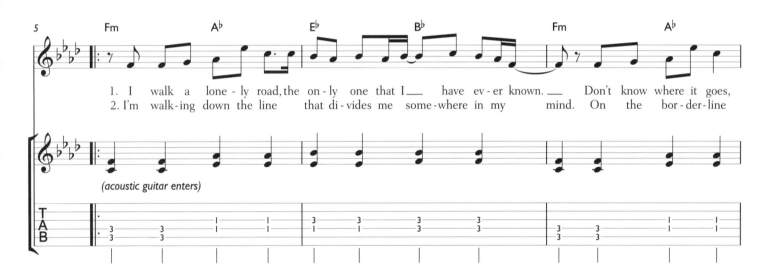

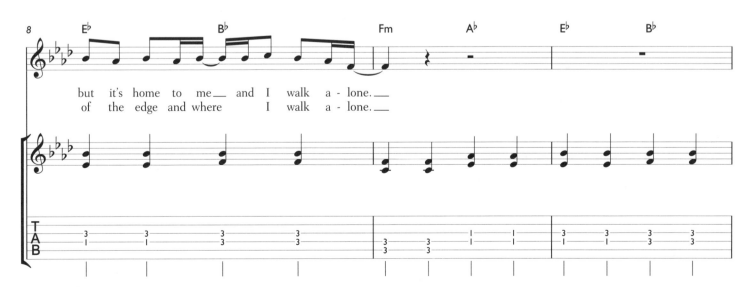

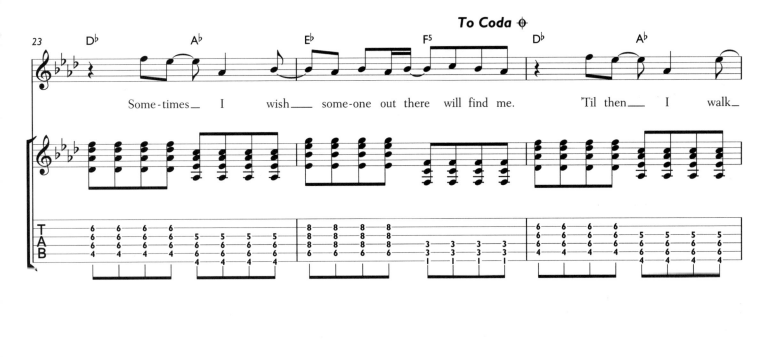

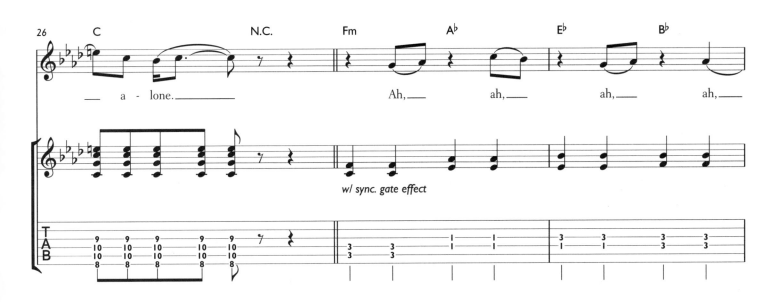

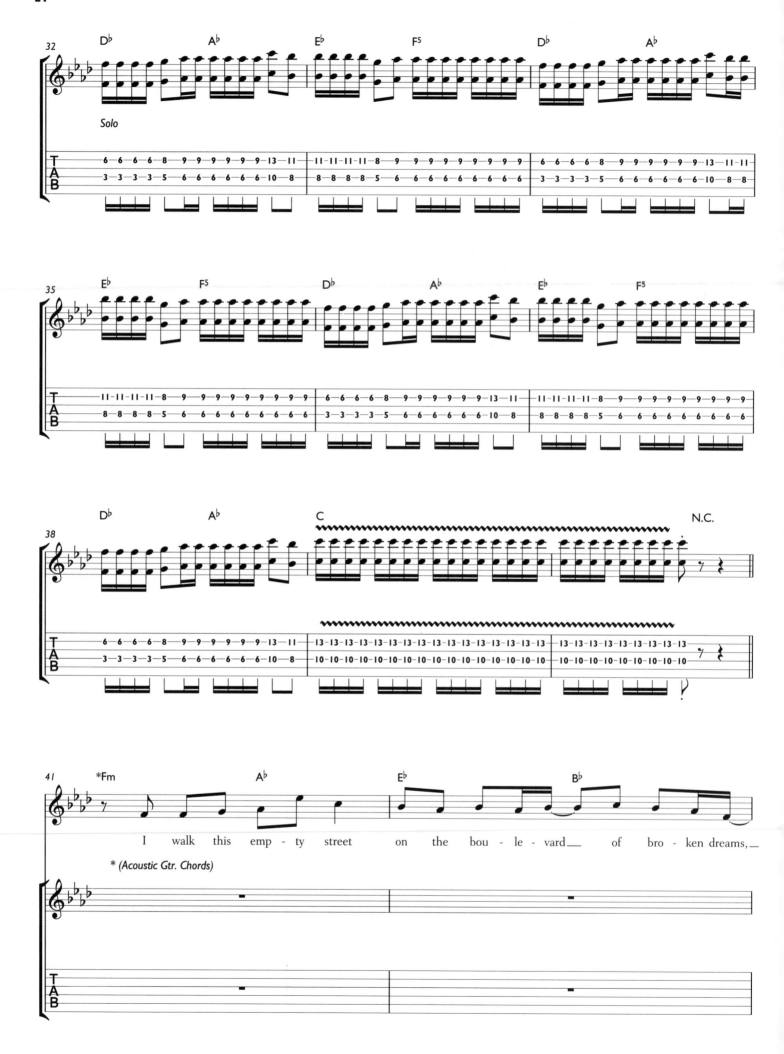

BRAIN STEW

WORDS AND MUSIC BY BILLIE JOE ARMSTRONG, FRANK E. WRIGHT III AND MICHAEL PRITCHARD

* Fretted notes only

GOOD RIDDANCE (TIME OF YOUR LIFE)

WORDS AND MUSIC BY BILLIE JOE ARMSTRONG, FRANK E. WRIGHT III AND MICHAEL PRITCHARD

So make the best___ of___ this test___ and don't ask why._____
Tat - toos of mem - o - ries,___ and dead___ skin on trial._____

It's not a quest - ion, but___ a les - son___ learned in___ time. }
For what it's worth,___ it___ was worth_____ all___ the___ while. }

It's

some-thing un - pre - dict - a - ble,___ but in the end___ is right.___

I

LONGVIEW

WORDS AND MUSIC BY BILLIE JOE ARMSTRONG, FRANK E. WRIGHT III AND MICHAEL PRITCHARD

Detune all strings
by a semitone

♩ = 145+ (variable)

1. I sit a-round and watch the tube, but noth-ing's on.
2. Peel me off this vel-cro seat and get me mov - ing.
3. I sit a-round and watch the phone but no-one's call - ing.

I change the chan-nels for an hour or two,
I sure as hell can't do it by my-self.
Call me pa-thet-ic, call me what you will.

twid-dle my thumbs just for a bit. I'm sick of all the same old shit;
I'm feel-ing like a dog in heat barred in-doors from the sum-mer street.
My moth-er says to get a job, but she don't like the one she's got.

in a house with un-locked doors, and I'm fuck-ing la - zy.
I locked the door to my own cell and I lost the key.
When mas-tur-ba - tion's lost it's fun you're fuck-ing lone - ly.

To Coda ⊕

TRACK 9
BACKING TRACK 18

MINORITY

WORDS AND MUSIC BY BILLIE JOE ARMSTRONG, FRANK E. WRIGHT III AND MICHAEL PRITCHARD

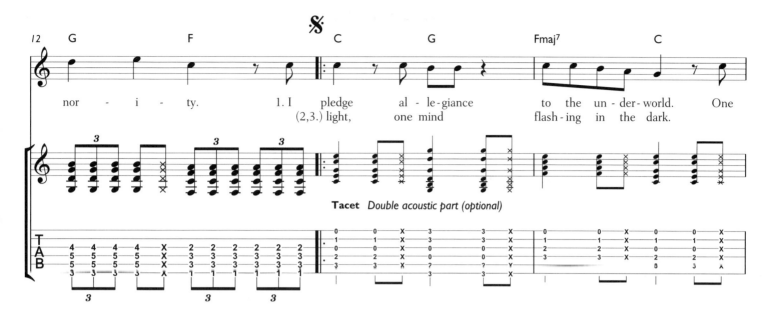

nor - i - ty.
1. I pledge al - le - giance to the un - der - world. One
(2,3.) light, one mind flash - ing in the dark.

Tacet *Double acoustic part (optional)*

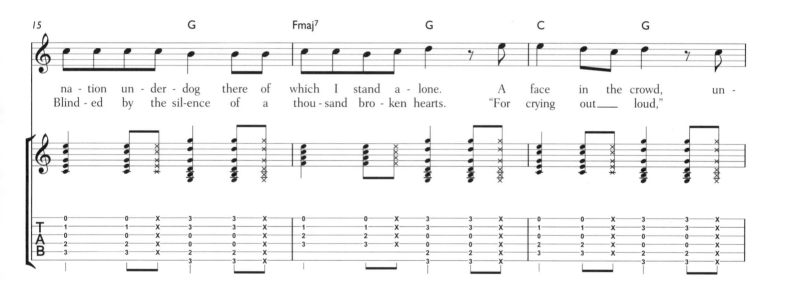

na - tion un - der - dog there of which I stand a - lone. A face in the crowd, un -
Blind - ed by the sil - ence of a thou - sand bro - ken hearts. "For crying out___ loud,"

sung a - gainst the mold. With - out a doubt, sin - gled out, the on - ly way I know. } 'Cause
she screamed un - to me. A free - for - all, fuck 'em all. "You are your own sight."

Gtr. enters

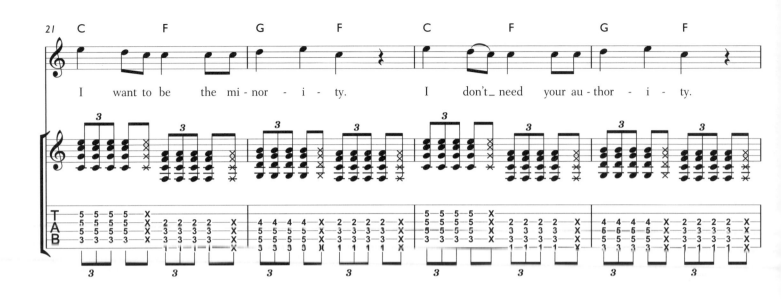

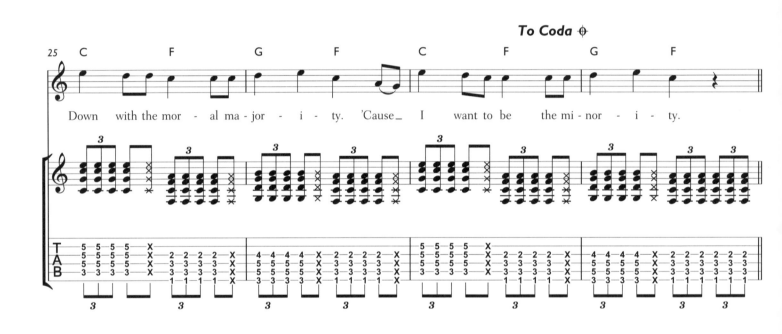

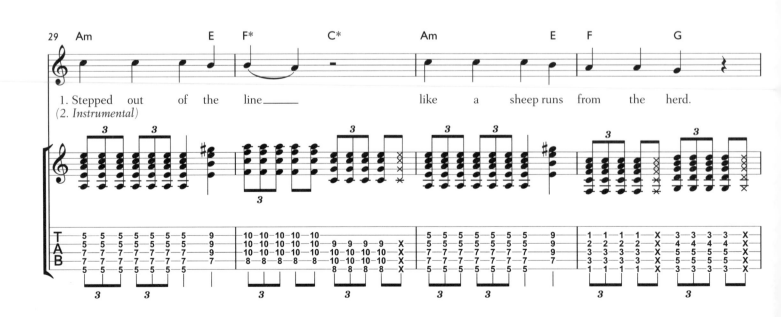

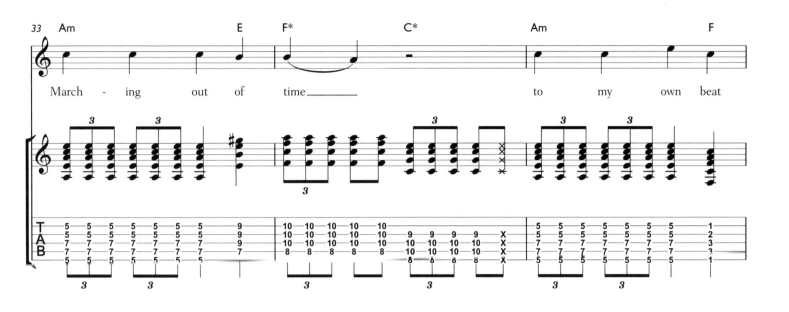

Marching out of time_____ to my own beat

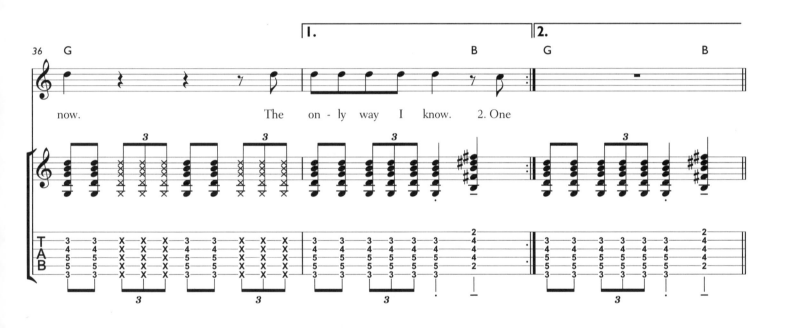

now. The only way I know. 2. One

D.%. al Coda

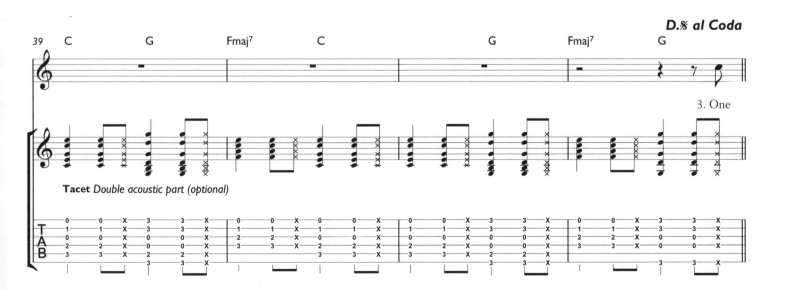

3. One

Tacet *Double acoustic part (optional)*

⊕ *Coda*

WAKE ME UP WHEN SEPTEMBER ENDS

WORDS AND MUSIC BY BILLIE JOE ARMSTRONG, MICHAEL PRITCHARD AND FRANK E. WRIGHT III

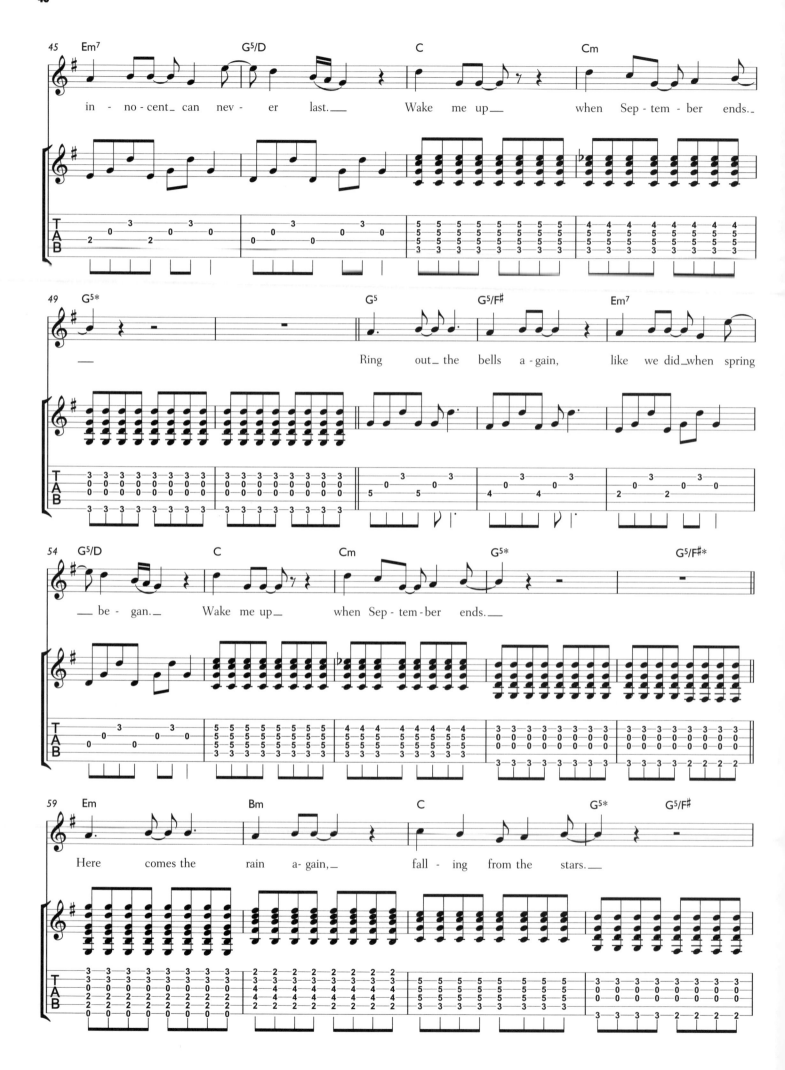

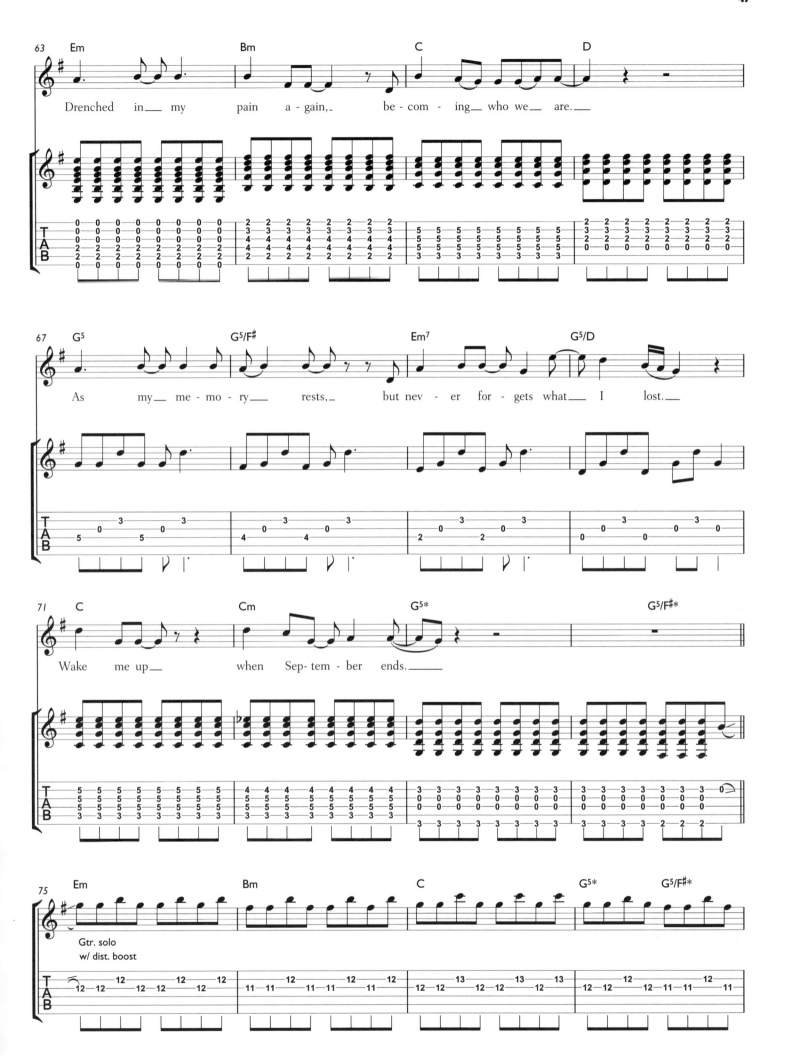

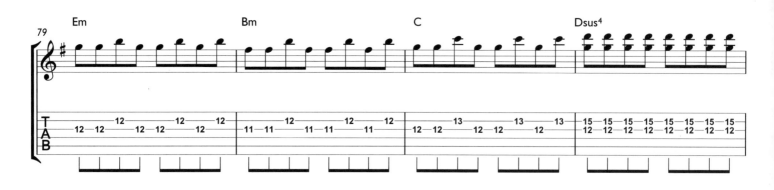

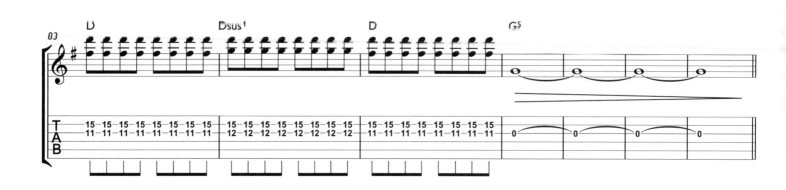

Sum - mer_ has come and passed, the in - no - cent_ can nev - er last._

Double acoustic gtr. part (optional)

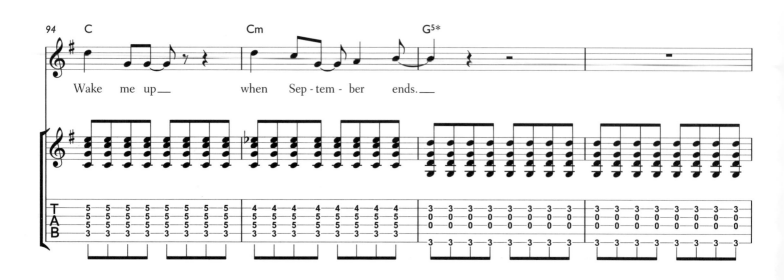

Wake me up_ when Sep - tem - ber ends._

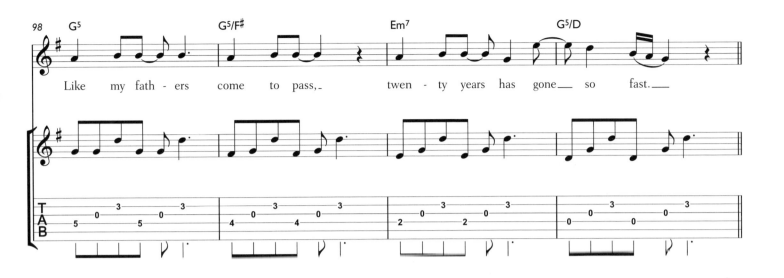

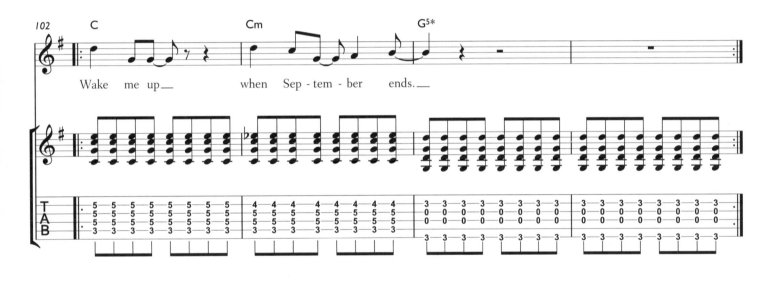

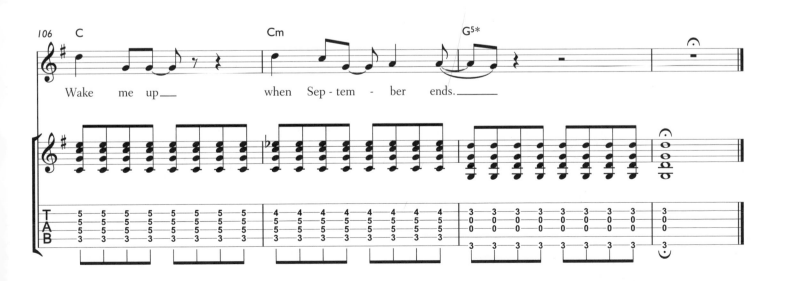

WHEN I COME AROUND

WORDS AND MUSIC BY BILLIE JOE ARMSTRONG, FRANK E. WRIGHT III AND MICHAEL PRITCHARD

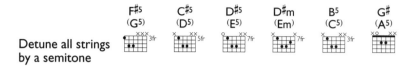

Detune all strings
by a semitone

1 bar count in

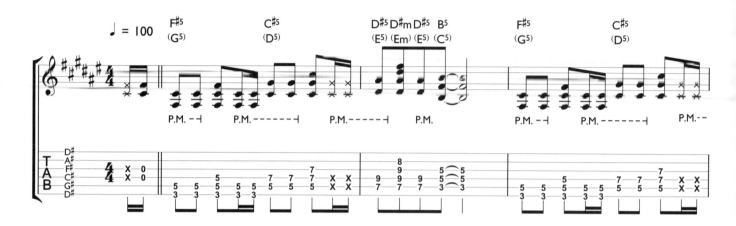

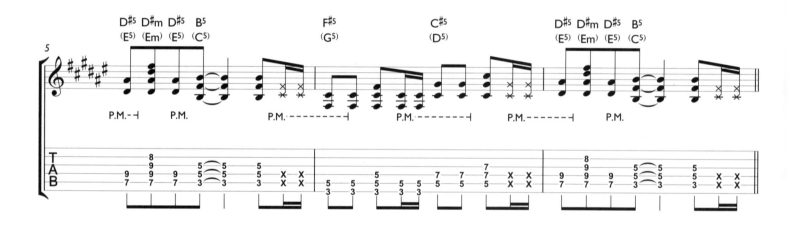

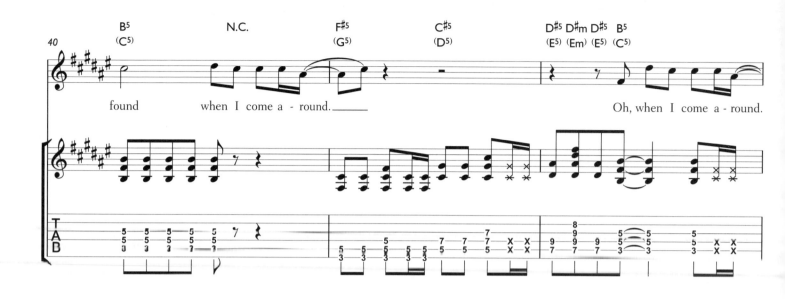

found   when I come a - round._____   Oh, when I come a - round.

Oh, when I come a - round._____

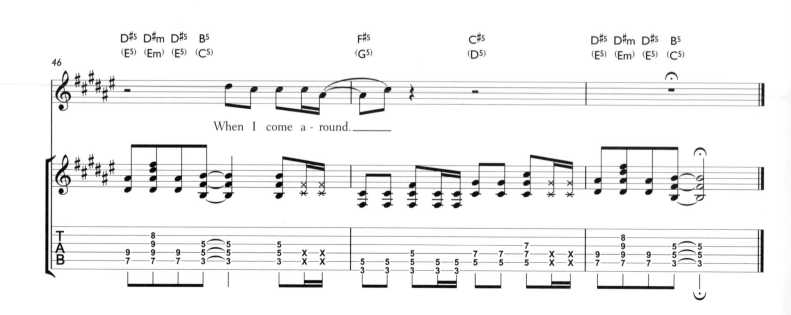

When I come a - round._____

Notation and Tablature explained

Understanding chord boxes

Chord boxes show the neck of your guitar as if viewed head on—the vertical lines represent the strings (low E to high E, from left to right), and the horizontal lines represent the frets.

An **X** above a string means 'don't play this string'.
An **O** above a string means 'play this open string'.
The black dots show you where to put your fingers.

A curved line joining two dots on the fretboard represents a 'barre'. This means that you flatten one of your fingers (usually the first) so that you hold down all the strings between the two dots at the fret marked.

A fret marking at the side of the chord box shows you where chords that are played higher up the neck are located.

Tuning your guitar

The best way to tune your guitar is to use an electronic tuner. Alternatively, you can use relative tuning; this will ensure that your guitar is in tune with itself, but won't guarantee that you will be in tune with the original track (or any other musicians).

How to use relative tuning

Fret the low E string at the 5th fret and pluck; compare this with the sound of the open A string. The two notes should be in tune. If not, adjust the tuning of the A string until the two notes match.

Repeat this process for the other strings according to this diagram:

Note that the B string should match the note at the 4th fret of the G string, whereas all the other strings match the note at the 5th fret of the string below.

As a final check, ensure that the bottom E string and top E string are in tune with each other.

Detuning and Capo use

If the song uses an unconventional tuning, it will say so clearly at the top of the music, e.g. '6 = D' (tune string 6 to D) or 'detune guitar down by a semitone'. If a capo is used, it will tell you the fret number to which it must be attached. The standard notation will always be in the key at which the song sounds, but the guitar tab will take tuning changes into account. Just detune/add the capo and follow the fret numbers. The chord symbols will show the sounding chord above and the chord you actually play below in brackets.

Use of figures

In order to make the layout of scores clearer, figures that occur several times in a song will be numbered, e.g. 'Fig. 1', 'Fig. 2', etc. A dotted line underneath shows the extent of the 'figure'. When a phrase is to be played, it will be marked clearly in the score, along with the instrument that should play it.

Reading Guitar Tab

Guitar tablature illustrates the six strings of the guitar graphically, showing you where you put your fingers for each note or chord. It is always shown with a stave in standard musical notation above it. The guitar tablature stave has six lines, each of them representing a different string. The top line is the high E string, the second line being the B string, and so on. Instead of using note heads, guitar tab uses numbers which show the fret number to be stopped by the left hand. The rhythm is indicated underneath the tab stave. Ex. 1 (below) shows four examples of single notes.

Ex. 2 shows four different chords. The 3rd one (Asus4) should be played as a barre chord at the 5th fret. The 4th chord (C9) is a half, or jazz chord shape. You have to mute the string marked with an 'x' (the A string in this case) with a finger of your fretting hand in order to obtain the correct voicing.

Ex.1

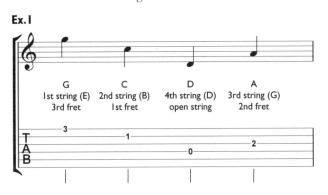

Ex.2

Notation of other guitar techniques

Picking hand techniques:

1. Down and up strokes

These symbols show that the first and third notes are to be played with a down stroke of the pick and the others up strokes.

2. Palm mute

Mute the notes with the palm of the picking hand by lightly touching the strings near the bridge.

3. Pick rake

Drag the pick across the indicated strings with a single sweep. The extra pressure will often mute the notes slightly and accentuate the final note.

4. Arpeggiated chords

Strum across the indicated strings in the direction of the arrow head of the wavy line.

5. Tremolo picking

Shown by the slashes on the stem of the note. Very fast alternate picking. Rapidly and continuously move the pick up and down on each note.

6. Pick scrape

Drag the edge of the pick up or down the lower strings to create a scraping sound.

7. Right hand tapping

'Tap' onto the note indicated by a '+' with a finger of the picking hand. It is nearly always followed by a pull-off to sound the note fretted below.

8. Tap slide

As with tapping, but the tapped note is slid randomly up the fretboard, then pulled off to the following note.

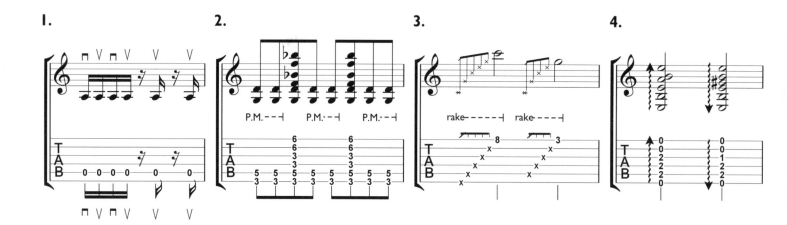

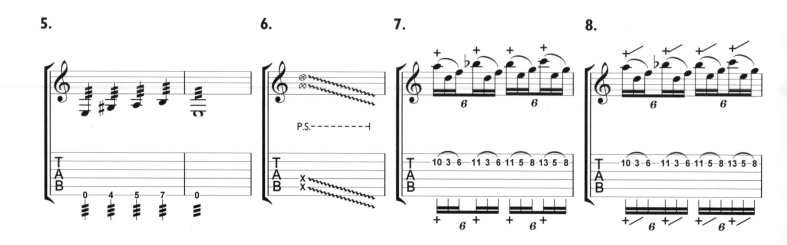